TYPES OF SCIENTISTS

A COLORING BOOK FOR ALL AGES

Semarhy Quiñones-Soto, PhD

ABOUT THIS WORK

Types of Scientists: A Coloring Book for All Ages aims to inform about different science fields, jobs and careers available to current and future scientists.

As a young person, I was not aware of the vast variety of science fields, educational requirements and different jobs available to scientist. This coloring book serves as a quick guide and resource to advising scientific careers, while providing pages to be creative with colors. It also aims to highlight and promote the visibility of women as professionals in science fields. These images of women in science are not meant to push these careers to young girls. Rather, it provides options for what is possible, because you cannot be what you cannot see.

As a Hispanic woman in science, my mission is to amplify our presence. My mother served as my role model. But, I recognize not everyone has a person or an image they can identify and follow. Knowing there are women currently working and being successful in science sends a message of possibilities and empowerment. This is also true for the women who currently work these fields. For them, images of women in science send a message of inclusiveness and belonging. In summary, representation matters.

THIS BOOK IS FOR MY MOM AND ALL WOMEN IN SCIENCE.

ABOUT THE ART

The illustrations in this coloring book are part of an online project, *Types of Scientists*, which the artist has been sharing through social media platforms. These illustrations are fantasy creations, envisioning women as STEAMpunk Scientists (where STEAM stands for science, technology, engineering, art and mathematics). Steampunk art is inspired by the industrial revolution, envisioning a future where steam engines and coils are the main technological advances. Steampunk art is characterized by images of cogs, machines and goggles. The illustrations in this coloring book are meant to be fun and informative.

ABOUT THE ARTIST

Instagram: @semarhyq.art
Twitter: @semarhyquinones
Website: www.semarhyquinones.com

Dr. Semarhy Quiñones-Soto is a bacterial geneticist and freelance artist. She was born and raised in Puerto Rico, where she earned her bachelor's degree in Microbiology from the University of Puerto Rico, Humacao. She obtained her Ph.D. degree in Microbiology from the University of California, Davis, where she studied the origin of mutations under stressful conditions. Currently, Dr. Quiñones-Soto works as a full-time biology lecturer at California State University, Sacramento. She also works as an academic advisor for the LSAMP & RISE Programs to help increase the number of students entering graduate programs. In addition to teaching, she is passionate about increasing the visibility of women in the sciences. She works her passion to develop a diverse pool of scientists by coordinating, advising and mentoring science students, and through community outreach and her artwork.

THE ABC'S OF TYPES OF SCIENTISTS...

When we talk about scientists, we may think of a person wearing a white coat, working in a lab, doing experiments. However, not all scientists wear a white coat! Moreover, not all scientists work in a lab. Some scientists work as communicators, lecturer, artists and policy makers. Some scientists work in offices, hospitals, boats, government agencies and even the great outdoors. They use their scientific skills to solve problems, communicate scientific findings or illustrate science-related images. This coloring book presents the ABC's of Types of Scientists in various science fields and job positions.

HOW TO CHOOSE YOUR TYPE OF SCIENTIST?

Some people learn at an early age what is their favorite science field. But, for most of us, it is not that easy. So, explore your options by taking classes, be a student researcher, talk to scientists working in different fields and positions, and find mentors to provide guidance and choices.

WHAT ARE SCIENCE FIELDS?

Science is divided into units called fields and organizes scientists with similar interests*. But, these fields can also merge. This coloring book presents some Types of Scientists who do not belong to one field. They work in multidisciplinary careers collaborating with other Types of Scientists.

EDUCATIONAL REQUIREMENTS...

This coloring book presents different Types of Scientists and the most common educational requirements needed to pursue each type as a career. However, each person is unique and their pathways will be as diverse as we are. So, while the most common pathways of education are described here, there are alternatives and various ways of achieving your career goals.

Descriptions of Degrees mentioned in this coloring book:
- **Associate's Degree** - degree awarded upon the completion of a two-year undergraduate program of study. It may be a career, technical or a transfer degree for students who transfer to a four-year bachelor's degree-granting school.
- **Bachelor's Degree** - degree awarded upon successful completion of an undergraduate program of at least four years of study.
- **Master's Degree** - degree awarded upon the successful completion of an advanced graduate program of study beyond the bachelor's degree.
- **Doctorate Degree** - also known as a Ph.D., it is the highest academic degree awarded upon successful completion of an advanced graduate program of study and the completion of scholarly research work presented in a dissertation.

A is for ASTRONOMER

An ASTRONOMER is a type of scientist who is passionate about the objects found in space, like planets, moons, stars and galaxies. They also seek to understand how the Universe was formed, how it has evolved and how it works. While astronomers are among the oldest types of scientists in history, they continue to make amazing discoveries.

How can YOU become an ASTRONOMER?
A person who wants to be an astronomer is curious and passionate about space and the objects found in it. To pursue a career as an astronomer, you should study mathematics, physics and astronomy related courses. After completing a bachelor's degree, you can continue your education to obtain a master's or a doctorate degree, depending on how far you want to go.

SHOOT FOR THE STARS!

Science Field: Astronomy
Related Types of Scientists: Astrophysicist, Cosmologists, Planetary Scientist

@SEMARHYQ.ART

ASTRONOMER

B is for BOTANIST

A BOTANIST is a type of scientist who studies plants. They may focus on different fields depending on their interests. Some botanists are interested in understanding how plants work, while others are interested in learning how plants interact with their environment. Some botanists focus on how plants can make better crops, while others want to discover how plants can be used to make medicine or fuel. Some botanists are interested in studying how plants get sick and others try to learn how to conserve them. It does not matter the reason why a botanist loves plants, there is an area of study that fits their passion.

How can YOU become a BOTANIST?
A person who wants to be a botanist would obtain a degree in a biological sciences field, like plant biology or general biology. With a bachelor's degree, a botanist could get a position working in laboratories, parks, plant nurseries, farms and research stations. A person could also obtain a master's or a doctorate degree in botany, which would allow them to work as a professor or researcher.

LET YOUR SCIENCE BLOOM!

Science Field: Botany
Related Types of Scientists: Agronomer, Plant Scientist, Phycologist

@SEMARHYQ.ART

BOTANIST

C is for CHEMIST

A CHEMIST is a type of scientist who studies the properties and characteristics of **matter** to gain an understanding on how chemical substances change when they are combined. Chemist can study existing chemical substances or even create new ones! Almost every major field in science depends on discoveries made by chemists, and our daily lives benefit from materials made by them.

How can YOU become a CHEMIST?
A person who wants to be a chemist would study chemistry or chemistry-related classes to obtain a bachelor's degree. With a bachelor's degree, a chemist could get a position working in a laboratory. A person could also obtain a master's or a doctorate degree in chemistry to obtain advanced positions.

THINK BEFORE YOU REACT!

Science Field: Chemistry
Related Types of Scientists: Biochemist, Analytical Chemist, Organic Chemist

CHEMIST

D is for DATA SCIENTIST

A DATA SCIENTIST is a type of scientist who interprets complex sets of **data** to extract what they mean and build creative models used to solve problems. A data scientist combines their computer, analytical and statistical skills to look for patterns, discover trends and suggest possible solutions. Data scientists can be found in education, government agencies, industry, finance, and commerce.

How can YOU become a DATA SCIENTIST?
A person who wants to be a data scientist is a person who likes to work with large amounts of information, use computers to solve complex problems and likes to look for patterns. To pursue a career as a data scientist, you would take classes related to computer sciences, computer engineering, applied mathematics, statistics and physics. A bachelor's degree would allow you to work as a data scientist. However, there are alternatives to the bachelor's degree, like certification programs or bootcamps, that will allow you to work as a data scientist. Obtaining a bachelor's degree and a subsequent master's or doctorate degree would allow you to advance in your career.

THE DATA SPEAKS TO ME!

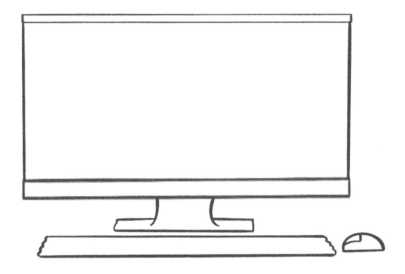

Science Field: Data Science
Related Types of Scientists: Coder, Data Management, Computer Scientist

@SEMARHYQ.ART

DATA SCIENTIST

E is for EPIDEMIOLOGIST

An EPIDEMIOLOGIST is a type of scientist who studies patterns and causes of health-related risks and occurrences in populations. Epidemiologists seek to understand the origin, spread and control of health risks, like infectious diseases, environmental pollutants or food-borne illnesses. They can work at research laboratories, hospitals, government agencies, private industry and pharmaceutical companies.

How can YOU become a EPIDEMIOLOGIST?
A person who wants to be an epidemiologist must obtain a bachelor's degree in biology, chemistry, public health or any field that includes statistics and health sciences, followed by a post-graduate degree, like a master's of science or a master's of public health. It is highly recommended to gain a few years' experience and complete certification programs to advance as an epidemiologist. You may continue your education and complete a doctor of medicine or a doctorate in science degree to work as a professional epidemiologist.

DETERMINED TO FIND THE CAUSE!

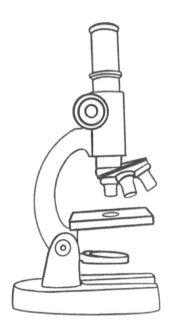

Science Field: Epidemiology
Related Types of Scientists: Microbiologist, Public Health Officials, Biostatistician

EPIDEMIOLOGIST

F is for FIELD SCIENTIST

Not all scientists work in a laboratory! A FIELD SCIENTIST is a type of scientist who works in the great outdoors, traveling to different regions around the world, exploring different land, air and water environments. They collect and analyze samples from a region, like soil, rocks, water and wildlife. It does not matter what type of science a field scientist chooses, there is an area of study for them to do their work.

How can YOU become a FIELD SCIENTIST?
A person who wants to be a field scientist must be comfortable working in the great outdoors in various weather conditions, spending lots of time traveling and collecting samples from nature. To pursue a career as a field scientist, you must first choose your science interest. After completing a bachelor's degree in your chosen science field, you could gain experience working in the great outdoors or continue your education by pursuing a master's or doctorate degree.

Loves the Great Outdoors!

Science Field: Multidisciplinary
Related Types of Scientists: Geologists, Marine Biologists, Anthropologists

@SEMARHYQ.ART

FIELD SCIENTIST

G is for GEOLOGIST

A GEOLOGIST is a type of scientist who studies the composition, structure, history and changes on Earth, as well as other planets. They study earthquakes, landslides, volcanoes, terrains, rocks, bodies of water, and materials and minerals found inside the earth. Geologist may also incorporate skills from other fields of science, like biology and chemistry, to do their work. You can find geologists at universities, government agencies, private industry and in the great outdoors.

How can YOU become a GEOLOGIST?
A person who wants to be a geologist will pursue a bachelor's degree in a geology-related field and complete classes with a specific interest to define their specialization. Your preparation may include classes in mathematics, computer sciences, geography and other sciences. You may continue your education to obtain a master's or a doctorate, which will allow you to become a specialist in your area of interest.

SCIENCE ROCKS!

Science Field: Geology
Related Types of Scientists: Volcanologist, Hydrologist, Petrologist

@SEMARHYQ.ART

GEOLOGIST

H is for HYDROLOGIST

A HYDROLOGIST is a type of scientist who studies the properties of bodies of water. They use their skills to understand the impact of humans on water quality, consumption and preservation. Hydrologists also collect water samples to study the composition of materials, minerals and pollutants. They can collaborate with other types of scientists, like biologist to study aquatic wildlife. They may also work with public officials to make policies for water conservation, water supply management and evaluate other water-related projects that affect society.

How can YOU become a Hydrologist?
A person who wants to be a hydrologist must complete a bachelor's degree in earth sciences, environmental sciences or natural sciences. Your education may include mathematics, statistics, computer sciences and data analysis. In addition to classes, you may need to learn how to use sophisticated equipment, geographic information systems (GIS) or global positioning system (GPS). You may need to complete certifications, a master's or doctorate degree to work as a professional hydrologist.

WATER IS LIFE!

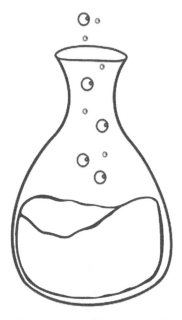

Science Field: Hydrology
Related Types of Scientists: Pedologist, Atmospheric Scientist, Wildfire Scientist

@SEMARHYQ.ART

HYDROLOGIST

I is for INDUSTRIAL SCIENTIST

Not all scientists work in academia! An INDUSTRIAL SCIENTIST is a type of scientist who performs deadline-oriented projects with a commercial focus, like biotechnology, manufacturing or food companies. They need to be detailed-oriented and keep records of their work. Industrial scientists must work in collaboration with others to solve problems, make better products and test the quality of current goods, to meet important deadlines.

How can YOU become a INDUSTRIAL SCIENTIST?
A person who wants to be an industrial scientist will have a bachelor's degree in a physical or natural science field, with classes in mathematics and statistics, and laboratory skills. If you want to advance into a supervisory role, you would need to complete a graduate degree, like a master's or a doctorate.

SCIENCE WORKS WHEN THE TEAM WORKS!

Science Field: Multidisciplinary
Related Types of Scientists: Pharmaceutical Scientist, Biomedical Scientist

@SEMARHYQ.ART

INDUSTRIAL SCIENTIST

J is for JUNIOR SCIENTIST

Not all scientists need a doctorate to work as scientists! A JUNIOR SCIENTIST is a type of scientist who works in research projects and is supervised by a research scientist called a principal investigator (PI). They can work in laboratories or in the great outdoors. Depending on the research project, the junior scientist may be responsible for operating sophisticated equipment, analyzing data, keeping records and writing reports. They work as part of a team with research staff, students and other scientists.

How can YOU become a JUNIOR SCIENTIST?
A person who works as a junior scientist has a bachelor's degree in their science field of interest and has experience working in independent research projects as a student. Most bachelor's of science degrees offer classes that prepare you to work as a junior scientist, with a combination of knowledge and skills that will enable you to solve problems using the scientific method.

YOU CAN SCIENCE!

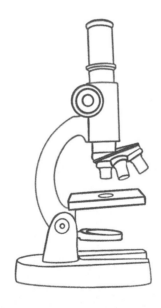

Science Field: Multidisciplinary
Related Types of Scientists: Researcher, Laboratory Assistant, Principal Investigator

JUNIOR SCIENTIST

@SEMARHYQ.ART

K is for KINESIOLOGIST

A KINESIOLOGIST is a type of scientist who look for ways to improve the human body by studying muscle movement. As a health scientist, kinesiologists seek to better understand the mechanisms of body movement to improve methods of physical therapy and address physiological concerns. Kinesiologists work with athletes, work-related injuries, as teachers and researchers.

How can YOU become a KINESIOLOGIST?
A person who wants to be a kinesiologist will complete a bachelor's degree in kinesiology or an exercise-related science. The completion of a and a master's degree in kinesiology is required to work as a professional kinesiologist as a consultant, a physical therapist or occupational therapist.

SCIENCE MOVES ME!

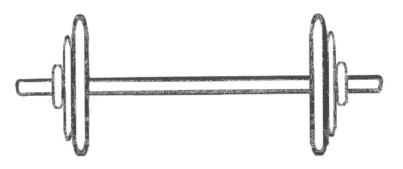

Science Field: Kinesiology
Related Types of Scientists: Exercise Scientist, Physiologist, Anatomist

@SEMARHYQ.ART

KINESIOLOGIST

L is for LAB TECHNICIAN

A LAB TECHNICIAN is a type of scientist who work in laboratories helping scientist: complete their projects, preparing the tools and materials for laboratory courses, or testing samples for medical diagnosis. They can be found in laboratories at universities, hospitals government agencies, industry and in the great outdoors. Lab technicians must keep records of their work, be detailed-oriented and have knowledge of safety regulations while working in a lab.

How can YOU become a LAB TECHNICIAN?
A person who wants to be a lab technician can earn an associate or a bachelor's degree in their area of interest to get an entry-level job. However, a graduate degree, like a master's degree, may be required to advance in your career and specialize in a particular area.

I AM HERE TO HELP!

Science Field: Multidisciplinary
Related Types of Scientists: Lab Manager, Lab Supervisor, Junior Scientist

@SEMARHYQ.ART

LAB TECHNICIAN

M is for MICROBIOLOGIST

A MICROBIOLOGIST is a type of scientist who studies the characteristics, growth and evolution of microorganisms, like **bacteria**, algae, fungi and any other living thing that cannot be seen with the naked eye. They study the response to and production of antibiotics by microorganisms, they prepare and maintain cultures of microorganisms for research and use products made by microorganisms to make goods for human use, like biofuel, medicine and food.

How can YOU become a MICROBIOLOGIST?

A person who wants to be a microbiologist must complete a bachelor's degree in microbiology or a biology-related field, with classes in chemistry, physics and mathematics. As a microbiology student, you may take also classes in microbial genetics, microbial physiology and environmental microbiology to learn what area of microbiology is of interest to you. To work as a research scientist or a professor, you will need to complete a doctorate in microbiology.

LOVES THE LITTLE THINGS IN LIFE!

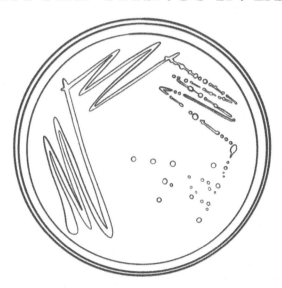

Science Field: Microbiology
Related Types of Scientists: Mycologist, Cell Biologist, Bacterial Geneticist

@SEMARHYQ.ART

MICROBIOLOGIST

N is for NEUROSCIENTIST

A NEUROSCIENTIST is a type of scientist who studies the nervous system, including the brain, spinal cord and nerves. They can focus their work in understanding how the nervous system functions, the cause and treatment of diseases, or conduct behavioral studies. While neuroscientist can use human brains in their studies, they can also use **model organisms** to perform experiments.

How can YOU become a NEUROSCIENTIST?
A person who wants to be a neuroscientist should complete a bachelor's degree in neurosciences or a related field. Depending on your focus, you will need a doctorate degree if you want to work as a research scientist or a doctorate in medicine if you want to work in a clinical setting. However, if you wish to do both research and treat patients, you can obtain a PhD/MD degree that would allow you to do research in a clinical setting.

FEED YOUR BRAIN!

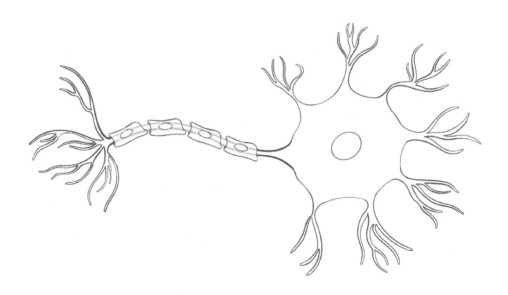

Science Field: Neurobiology
Related Types of Scientists: Cell Biologist, Molecular Biologist, Geneticist

@SEMARHYQ.ART

NEUROSCIENTIST

35

O is for OCEANOGRAPHER

An OCEANOGRAPHER is a type of scientist who studies the oceans, from its wildlife, to the seafloor, its ecosystems and chemical properties. About 70% of the Earth's surface is covered by oceans. Oceanographers are field scientists, spending their time in the water, collecting samples or taking measures on site. They can spend their time on a boat, under water as divers or at a research station.

How can YOU become an OCEANOGRAPHER?
A person who wants to be an oceanographer would complete a bachelor's degree in marine or related science, taking classes in chemistry, physics and biology. Depending on your focus, you may want to study geology and computer science. You can obtain entry-level internships with a bachelor's degree. However, to work as an oceanographer, you may need to further your education with a master's or a doctorate, which will allow you to work as a principal scientist.

EN EL MAR, LA VIDA ES MÁS SABROSA.

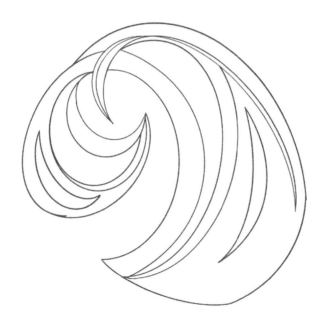

Science Field: Oceanography
Related Types of Scientists: Meteorologist, Climate Scientist, Marine Biologist

@SEMARHYQ.ART

OCEANOGRAPHER

P is for PHYSIOLOGIST

A PHYSIOLOGIST is a type of scientist who studies the human anatomy. They are interested in understanding how the **organ systems** work, how they work together with other systems in your body and how they are affected by outside agents, like how smoke affects your lungs. They can be found in different work environments, including teaching at universities or working with health teams at clinics.

How can YOU become a PHYSIOLOGIST?

A person who wants to be a physiologist must complete a bachelor's degree focusing on anatomy, physiology or a biology related science. With a bachelor's, you can work as a junior scientists or lab technician at en entry-level position. There are some opportunities to advance if you complete a master's degree. But, if you wish to work as a researcher in industry or work at universities, you should complete a doctorate degree. Alternatively, you can also work as a physiologist at a clinic or hospital if you complete a doctorate in medicine.

LET'S WORK TOGETHER!

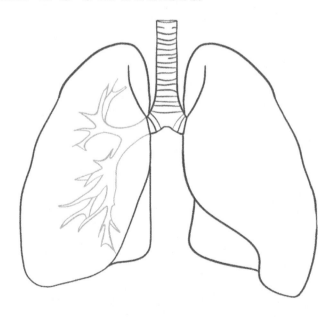

Science Field: Physiology
Related Types of Scientists: Anatomist, Comparative Mammalogist, Pharmacologist

PHYSIOLOGIST

Q is for QUANTUM PHYSICIST

A QUANTUM PHYSICIST is a type of scientist who wants to understand how the Universe works by studying the smallest pieces of **matter**, the **atoms**. These atoms are so small, we cannot see them with our naked eyes. Quantum physicists use special tools, like microscopes, to study them.

How can YOU become a QUANTUM PHYSICIST?
A person who wants to be a quantum physicist must enjoy solving complex puzzles. They will complete a bachelor's degree in physics, along with classes in mathematics, mechanics and electricity. With a bachelor's, you may obtain an entry-level junior scientist or technician job. If you wish to advance as a researcher, you may obtain a master's degree. A doctoral degree in physics will allow you to work as a principal investigator or work as a professor in quantum physics.

TINY BUT MIGHTY!

Science Field: Quantum Physics
Related Types of Scientists: Theoretical Physicist, Particle Physicist

@SEMARHYQ.ART

QUANTUM PHYSICIST

R is for RESEARCHER

A RESEARCHER is a type of scientist who performs experiments to increase the current body of scientific knowledge by using the **scientific method**. They plan and carry out experiments, collect and analyze data, summarize and report their results, and communicate to the public their conclusions. You can find researchers in laboratories or any other space for investigation at universities, industries, hospitals, government agencies, private sector and the great outdoors. Researchers can be employed at all levels, from students to professionals, from entry-level positions to administrators.

How can YOU become a RESEARCHER?

Any type of scientist can be a researcher, but not all scientists work in research. If you want to work as a researcher, you can start by seeking opportunities while working towards your bachelor's degree. As an undergraduate researcher, you will gain experience and work with faculty researchers, who will mentor your education. If you wish to pursue a career as a research scientist, you must complete a doctorate in your favorite area of science. Some fields may require additional post-doctoral work.

STAY CALM & RESEARCH ON!

Science Field: Multidisciplinary
Related Types of Scientists: Principal Investigator, Junior Scientist

RESEARCHER

@SEMARHYQ.ART

S is for SCIENCE COMMUNICATOR

Not all scientists work in a lab! There are a wide range of opportunities, jobs and careers, where you can apply your scientific training. A SCIENCE COMMUNICATOR is a type of scientist who uses their communication skills to inform about scientific discoveries, content and unresolved problems to different audiences. They are experts in different communication platforms, including social media, and use their scientific and storytelling skills to explain complex topics to all types of audiences, even non-scientific ones.

How can YOU become a SCIENCE COMMUNICATOR?
Any type of scientist can be a science communicator. In fact, many employed scientists also work as science communicators. Science Communication is a relatively new area born from the need to communicate complex scientific findings to general audiences. A science communicator must be empathetic, a great listener and culturally informed. They must also be able to adapt their message depending on their audience. They can work as bloggers, sciences writers, seminar speakers or social media.

SHARPEN YOUR COMMUNICATION SKILLS!

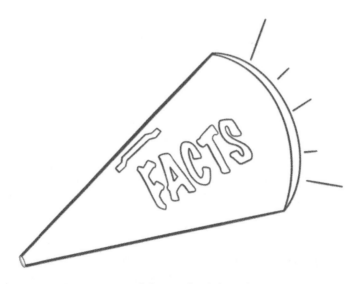

Science Field: Multidisciplinary
Related Types of Scientists: Political Scientist, Science Artist, Entrepreneur

SCIENCE COMMUNICATOR

T is for TOXICOLOGIST

A TOXICOLOGIST is a type of scientist who studies the effects of drugs, toxins and othe chemical agents may have on living things. They perform experiments to determine dosage or safe exposure limits of chemicals as well as factors that may influence their effect, like age gender and route of exposure. You may find toxicologists working in research labs, teaching classes, as expert witnesses in courtrooms, as policy makers and regulation agencies.

How can YOU become a TOXICOLOGIST?
A person who wants to be a toxicologist must complete a bachelor's degree in chemistry biology or biochemistry. With a bachelor's degree, you can work as a lab assistant or junior scientist. With a master's degree, you can work in a supervisory position or work as a lecturer With a doctorate degree, you can advance to work as a principal investigator in laboratories ranging from universities to the federal government.

WHAT DOESN'T KILL YOU!

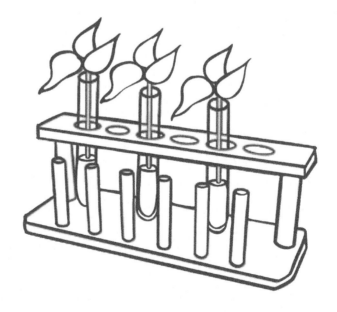

Science Field: Toxicology
Related Types of Scientists: Pharmacologist, Biochemist, Epidemiologist

TOXICOLOGIST

U is for UNDERREPRESENTED

The word **underrepresented** is used to define groups of individuals whose education and employment in the sciences are present in lower numbers compared to their representation in the U.S. population. These groups include women, persons with disabilities, and Black and African Americans, Hispanics and Latinos, American Indians and Alaska Natives*. For example, Black or African American women, who represent 12.2% of women in the U.S. population, hold 4.2% of science Ph.D. degrees; Latinas or Hispanic women, who represent 13.7% of women in the U.S. population, hold 5.8% of science Ph.D. degrees; and, American Indian or Alaska Native women, who represent 0.6% of women in the U.S. population, hold less than 0.3% of science Ph.D. degrees. In response to the lack of Black women, women of color and all individuals who identify as women who study, work or love science, the images of this coloring book are meant to over represent them!

YOU CANNOT BE WHAT YOU CANNOT SEE!

@SEMARHYQ.ART

UNDERREPRESENTED

V is for VIROLOGIST

A VIROLOGIST is a type of scientist who studies viruses, which are agents that infec humans and other animals, plants, fungi and bacteria. Their work can focus on differen aspects of the viruses, from how the survive inside their host to how to prevent illness. A virologist may work as a researcher at universities, government agencies, industry or clinics Due to the infectious nature of some viruses, virologists must be extra cautious in handlin samples and follow lab regulations.

How can YOU become a VIROLOGIST?
A person who wants to be a virologist must complete a bachelor's degree in microbiology or a biology-related field, with classes in chemistry, physics and mathematics. With a bachelor's you can work as a junior scientists or lab technician at en entry-level position. But, if yo wish to work as a researcher, you should complete a doctorate degree followed by post doctoral work. Alternatively, you can also work as a virologist at a clinic if you complete a doctorate in medicine.

IS IT ALIVE?

Science Field: Virology
Related Types of Scientists: Microbiologist, Immunologist, Epidemiologist

@SEMARHYQ.ART

VIROLOGIST

W is for WILDFIRE SCIENTIST

A WILDFIRE SCIENTIST is a type of scientist who studies the cause, consequences, benefits and prevention of wildfires. Their work helps us understand and manage these catastrophic events, inform government officials on policy making and predict potential hot spots. Wildfire scientists can work in fire labs or research stations across the country at the local, state and Federal agencies.

How can YOU become a WILDFIRE SCIENTIST?
A person who wants to be a wildfire scientist will need a bachelor's in forestry or an ecology related field with practical work experience. After a bachelor's, you may need to complete additional training and certificates depending on your interests. If you wish to pursue academic or research jobs, then you should complete a graduate degree, like a master's or a doctorate.

SCIENCE IS THE SPARK OF KNOWLEDGE!

Science Field: Wildfire Science
Related Types of Scientists: Fire Ecologist, Climate Scientist, Geologist

@SEMARHYQ.ART

WILDFIRE SCIENTIST

X is for X-Ray Crystallographer

An X-RAY CRYSTALLOGRAPHER is a type of scientist who study the molecular and atomic structures by using a tool that shoots a beam of X-rays. They work in many disciplines, like biology, chemistry and geology, and can be found in laboratories at universities, industry and research institutes.

How can YOU become an X-RAY CRYSTALLOGRAPHER?
A person who wants to be a X-ray crystallographer would complete a bachelor's degree in their favorite area of science and include classes in biology, chemistry, physics and computer sciences. Working as a student researcher with x-ray crystallography will give you experience and lab skills needed to obtain a position as a lab technician or junior scientist. However, completing a doctorate degree will allow you to work as a principal investigator or teach at a university.

Atoms Make Up Everything!

Science Field: Multidisciplinary
Related Types of Scientists: Biochemist, Biophysicist

@SEMARHYQ.ART

X-RAY CRYSTALLOGRAPHER

Y is for YEAST SCIENTIST

A YEAST SCIENTIST is a type of scientist who designs experiments using yeasts as their **model organism**. Yeast are living things made up of just one cell and are one of the best studied organisms. While it may seem that yeast and humans are nothing alike, many scientific discoveries about human biology have been made by using yeasts. For example, humans and yeast share many basic cell properties, like a nucleus inside their cells.

What is a MODEL ORGANISM?
A model organism is a non-human, living thing that has been used by scientists because they can be easily grown, maintain and reproduce for research purposes. Some model organisms have similar cellular properties when compared to humans, which enables scientists to make discoveries about human biology without the need to use humans. Other model organisms used in science include frogs, fruit flies, mice, rats, worms and fish.

NOT ALL MODELS WORK THE RUNWAY!

Science Field: Multidisciplinary
Related Types of Scientists: Developmental Biologist, Geneticist, Neuroscientist

@SEMARHYQ.ART

YEAST SCIENTIST

Z is for ZOOLOGIST

A ZOOLOGIST is a type of scientist who studies the life, reproduction, behavior and habita of animals. They may have a preferred animal or may study groups of them. Zoologist can be found in the great outdoors, working at zoos or aquariums, or doing research i laboratories, research stations or private industries.

How can YOU become a ZOOLOGIST?
A person who wants to be a zoologist will complete a bachelor's degree in a biology relate field with chemistry, physics, mathematics classes, as well as courses in zoology, organisma biology and molecular biology. While working towards your bachelor's, it is recommende you seek internships or other work opportunities to gain skills working in the field. bachelor's degree will allow you to obtain entry-level positions and assist in zoology projects A graduate degree, like a master's or doctorate, will allow you to advance in your career as principal investigator or supervisor.

I HEART ANIMALS!

Science Field: Zoology
Related Types of Scientists: Primatologist, Entomologist, Wildlife Biologist

@SEMARHYQ.ART

ZOOLOGIST

Glossary

Atom - smallest unit of matter.

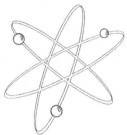

Bacteria - microscopic one-cell organisms found in almost all environments. They come in many shapes, can be both useful and harmful to humans depending on the type. Some bacteria are used to make our food, like yogurt. Some bacteria can make us sick, like a sore throat.

Communicator - a person who is skilled at delivering information and ideas to an audience.

Data - facts, numbers or information.

Degree - an academic title conferred after the completion of a program of study.

Facts - something known to exist, a truth.

Geode - a cavity inside a rock lined with crystals or minerals.

Graduate - a program or person involved in a program of study after completing a bachelor's degree.
Industrial - related to workers in a productive and commercial enterprise or industry.

Matter - something that occupies space.

Microscope - a laboratory instrument with magnifying lenses used to observe objects and living things that are too small to see with the naked eye.

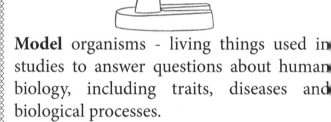

Model organisms - living things used in studies to answer questions about human biology, including traits, diseases and biological processes.

Multidisciplinary - composed of different fields of expertise.

Neuron - also called a nerve cell. It is a special type of cell that works as part of the nervous system. Its job is to deliver messages from the brain to other nerve cells throughout your body.

Organ System - a group of organs that work together to perform a particular function in body. For example, the circulatory system composed of the heart, arteries, veins and capillaries that work together to carry and deliver the blood.

Organ - a collection of tissues that perform particular function. For example, the human heart.

Organisms - a form of life. For example, bacteria, fungi, plants, animals and humans.

Petri Plate - a shallow cylindrical glass or plastic container with a lid used to hold growth medium to maintain bacterial or cell cultures.

Principal Investigator - PI, individual in charge of designing, developing and managing a research project.

Quantum - the smallest unit of radiant energy.

Research - the act of investigation into a particular subject to answer questions, solve problems and make discoveries.

Science - a body of knowledge or collection of facts about how our Universe works.

Scientific Method - a detailed process where a problem is identified, a hypothesis is proposed and tested, data is gathered and analyzed, and conclusions are made and shared.

Scientist - an individual who is en expert or works in science.

Undergraduate - a program or person who has not received a bachelor's degree.

Underrepresented - to be represented in disproportionately low numbers.

Virus - a microscopic infectious agent that needs to invade a living host to replicate.

SOURCES

- Casadevall A, Fang FC. 2015. Field Science—the Nature and Utility of Scientific Fields. mBio 6(5):e01259-15. doi:10.1128/mBio.01259-15
- National Science Foundation, National Center for Science and Engineering Statistics, National Survey of College Graduates, 2017

Websites:
- American Astronomical Society – www.aas.org
- American Chemical Society - www.acs.org
- American Society for Microbiology – www.asm.org
- Britannica - www.britannica.com
- The Big Story: The Petri Dish - www.thebiomedicalscientist.net/science
- Career Explorer – www.careerexplorer.com/careers
- Center for Disease Control and Prevention – www.cdc.gov
- Dictionary - www.dictionary.com
- Environmental Science – www.environmentalscience.org

ACKNOWLEDGMENTS

I would like to express my thanks to my friend and fellow Puerto Rican woman in science, Dr. Enid González-Orta, and my dear husband, Dr. Drew Reams, for your valuable constructive criticism in the development of this project. To my brother and graphic designer, Frankie Quiñones-Soto, for his help with the formatting and hints on how to work with publishing softwares. To Dr. Ahna Skop for your advise to make this project a reality.

I would like to give my special thanks to all my students, mentees, colleagues and fellow women in science, who work twice as hard to earn their seat at the table. May you pave the way for others to follow.